Contents

How to Use This Book

Vocabulary Development is a literacy tool that is meant to help learners achieve success in language arts. The activities were designed to be age appropriate and are based on curricula. Whenever possible, the nonfiction subject matter of the activities is based on social studies and science subjects that enhance the learning process. The activities follow the National Council of Teachers of English (NCTE) standards for developing word identification, sentence structure, context, spelling, editorial, and word recognition skills. These are the skills learners rely upon for success in reading comprehension and writing. *Vocabulary Development* will help learners perfect skills needed for communicating effectively as well as interpreting texts.

The six sections of *Vocabulary Development* are Vocabulary, Decoding Words, Spelling, Editing, Writing Sentences, and Word Relations. Each section focuses on developing specific vocabulary skills. For example, the Spelling section covers homophones, homographs, and contractions. Each activity is preceded by skill definitions and directions that make it fun to work through and an enjoyable learning experience.

Vocabulary

This section deals with developing vocabulary through context meaning, recognition of words through images, and understanding new words. As learners work through these activities, they will build important word-definition skills.

Decoding Words

The activities and skills in this section teach word definition and spelling through prefixes and suffixes. The activities teach learners to define words by understanding the meanings of prefixes and suffixes.

▰▶ Spelling

Homophones, homographs, and contractions often present special spelling challenges to learners. By conquering spelling challenges, learners will be able to tune their writing skills. These activities, which are coupled with curricula-based skills, can be used to supplement classroom learning.

▰▶ Editing

The editorial skills that are dealt with in this section allow learners to correct and improve their own writing. Being able to check spelling and capitalization and apply proper punctuation—question marks, periods, and commas—lets learners write clearly. Also, performing these skills properly as well as understanding their functions within sentences strengthens reading comprehension.

▰▶ Writing Sentences

This section deals with important grammar skills that are necessary for learners as they build writing skills. Learners must know how to create complete sentences as well as use a variety of sentence styles. The activities involve recognizing incomplete sentences, differentiating statements, questions, and exclamations, and using conjunctions.

▰▶ Word Relations

Classification, synonyms, and antonyms are important to developing vocabulary. These activities encourage learners to use language effectively by teaching them how to diversify words and apply them to their writing.

Name _____

Vocabulary

Context is used to figure out the meaning of an unknown word. Context is the other words in the sentence that help explain the word's meaning.

➡️ **Directions: Use the context to figure out the meaning of the underlined word. Write the word's meaning in the space provided.**

1 I liked the <u>topic</u> of our class lesson today, since the subject is interesting.

_____

2 When the clothes did not fit in her <u>luggage</u>, Jenny thought about buying another suitcase.

_____

3 The teacher <u>posted</u> the chart too high for the students to see, so she had to hang it lower.

_____

4 There was such a great <u>variety</u> of flowers at the market, I had trouble choosing from the many different kinds.

_____

5 The team was <u>successful</u> this year, winning almost every game.

_____

4

Name _____

Decoding Words

A prefix is a word part added to the beginning of a word to make a new word.

Directions: Use the prefixes and the root words below to make new words. Write the definition of the word next to it.

Prefix	Prefix Meaning	Root Words
re	again	place
un	opposite, or to do the opposite	sure
		fair
pre	before	test
		set
		load

_____   _____   _____

_____   _____   _____

_____   _____   _____

5

Name _____

Spelling

Homophones are words that sound the same but are spelled differently and have different meanings.

Directions: Choose the correct word to finish each sentence below.

1 We have to pay a _____ (*fare, fair*) before we can enter the carnival.

2 I have _____ (*too, two*) brothers named Brian and Jordan.

3 Emily has brown, curly _____ (*hare, hair*).

4 The family saw a _____ (*bear, bare*) while they were camping in the woods.

5 There is something in my _____ (*I, eye*).

6

Name _____

Editing

Proper punctuation and capitalization are necessary to help you understand what you read.

✏ Directions: Rewrite each pair of sentences with the correct punctuation and capitalization.

1 deserts have very little rainfall there are two types of deserts

_____

_____

2 what are the two types of deserts there are hot deserts and cold deserts

_____

_____

3 the mojave is a desert in the united states the mojave is a hot desert

_____

_____

4 cold deserts do not get hot the gobi is a cold desert

_____

_____

Name _____

Writing Sentences

*The word **and** is a conjunction. Conjunctions are words that connect parts of sentences.*

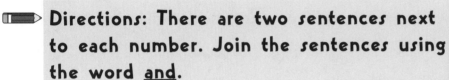

Directions: There are two sentences next to each number. Join the sentences using the word **and**.

1 Television cameras break up images into tiny parts. They record the images.

_____

_____

2 The tiny images are turned into signals. Antennas send the signals through the air.

_____

_____

3 A picture tube inside the television set puts the signals together. The picture tube makes pictures appear on the TV screen.

_____

_____

8

Name _____

Word Relations

Classifying is a way to group words, making them easy to identify.

Directions: Circle the word in each box that names the group to which the other words belong.

1 dandelion tulip flower rose	**2** piano saxophone clarinet instrument	**3** feeling angry excited cranky
4 ruby diamond emerald gem	**5** joint elbow knee wrist	**6** cinnamon spice pepper salt

9

Background

• The activities in this section help learners work on building vocabulary skills. The Vocabulary in Context sections (pp. 11–12) allow learners to practice defining a word by using clues from other words in the sentence or paragraph. The Words and Images (p. 13) activity gives the learners an opportunity to define words by connecting the meaning of the words to pictures. In New Words (p. 14), learners will define age-appropriate words while working on vocabulary skills.

Homework Helper

• Make a list of five age-appropriate words that are related in subject matter. Ask the learners to write a short essay that uses the words to tell about the subject.

Research-based Activity

• Have the learners use the library to find more information about tadpoles. Ask them to write about the different growth stages from tadpoles to frogs (p. 11).

Test Prep

• Vocabulary building is part of state standards throughout the United States. The vocabulary-building subjects of the activities in the section prepare learners for testing methods used in state-mandated testing.

Different Audiences

• To help English-as-a-Second-Language (ESL) learners, have them translate the sentences for the second Vocabulary in Context activity (p. 12). This will make grasping concepts in the English language easier.

Name _____

Vocabulary in Context

When you come across a word you do not know, use the words around it to help you figure out its definition. These surrounding words are known as the **context**.

Example: *The dog* <u>groomed</u> *itself by licking its fur to get rid of dirt. You can use the context of the sentence to figure out what* groomed *means. The rest of the sentence states that the dog licked its fur to get rid of dirt. We might also say that the dog cleaned itself. Therefore we can draw the conclusion that* groomed *means* cleaned.

Directions: Use the context of the sentences below to figure out the meaning of the words that are underlined. Write the meaning on the line under each sentence.

1 Frogs lay their eggs in ponds. <u>Tadpoles</u> <u>hatch</u> from the eggs.

_____

2 Tadpoles live in water and breathe through <u>gills</u>.

_____

3 Tadpoles <u>develop</u> legs as they grow into frogs.

_____

Name _____

Vocabulary in Context

*When you come across a word you do not know, use the words around it as clues to help you figure out the definition of the difficult word. These surrounding words are known as the **context**.*

Directions: Read the sentences below. Use the context to figure out the meaning of the underlined words. Write the meanings of the words on the lines.

1 The construction workers poured <u>cement</u> over the hole in the road. The clay substance will harden to fill the hole.

_____

2 Susan drove her car across the <u>overpass.</u> She knew it would take less time to drive across the bridge than to drive around the lake.

_____

3 Ella was given the <u>role</u> of the princess in the school play. She will study her lines and play that part well.

_____

4 The clown <u>entertained</u> us at the birthday party. He played games and did tricks to make us happy.

_____

Challenge: Suppose your friend missed class the day you learned about context. Explain to her, in your own words, how to use context to figure out word meanings.

Name _____

Words and Images

Pictures can help us figure out the meanings of words we don't know.

Directions: Choose the word from the box that names each part of the picture below. Write the name of the object on the line. Use the words you are sure about first and then figure out the rest.

| keyboard | mouse | screen | keys | monitor |

1 _____

2 _____

3 _____

4 _____

5 _____

Challenge: Go to your school library and look at the computers. Are there any other parts you can name?

Name _____

New Words

| regular | delicious | concentrate |
| reply | annoy | silent |

ACROSS

1 very tasty

2 without noise

3 answer

4 normal

DOWN

1 to focus your thoughts on one thing

2 bother

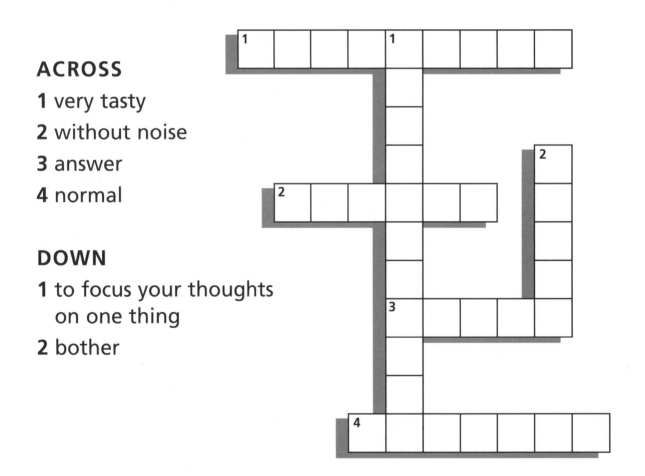

Challenge: One of the vocabulary words you just used is *delicious.* Think of a food that you would describe as *delicious.* Draw a picture of that food.

14

Name _____

Skill Check—Vocabulary
Vocabulary in Context

Directions: Use the context to figure out the meaning of the underlined word. Write the word's meaning in the space provided.

1 Dad <u>prepares</u> breakfast. He gets it ready for our family.

_____

2 We will <u>ship</u> the package to her. We will send it tomorrow.

_____

3 At the park, Mom and I <u>toss</u> a ball back and forth. We have fun throwing the ball to each other.

_____

Words and Images

Directions: Choose a word from the box to name each item below.

globe   United States   continent   equator

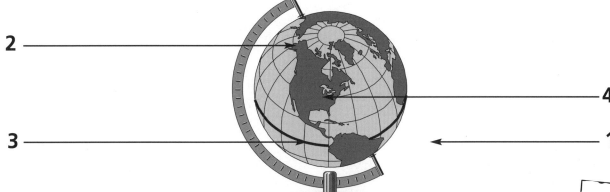

2 _____

3 _____

4

1

Teaching Tips...

TEACHING TIPS

Background

• Being able to decode words helps learners understand language structure. The activities in this section focus on spelling, by defining prefixes and suffixes. Building words by using prefixes and suffixes widens learners' vocabulary, hence enhancing their ability to communicate in written language.

Homework Helper

• Working together with the learners, create a prefix flower like the one on page 19. Use the prefix *pre* to create new words. Have learners write sentences using the new words.

Research-based Activity

• Working with prefixes and suffixes is a great opportunity for learners to become familiar with using a dictionary. Ask learners to find new words in the dictionary that begin with the prefix *mis*. Then ask them to find new words ending with the suffix *ous*.

Test Prep

• The activities in this section provide learners with an opportunity to experience subject matter that is dealt with in state testing as well as test formats that appear nationwide.

Different Audiences

• When working with accelerated learners, challenge them by raising the level of difficulty of words that use suffixes and prefixes. Make a list of words that use the suffixes and prefixes that appear on pages 17 and 20. Have accelerated learners try to define the words by using just the meanings of the root words and their prefixes and suffixes.

Name _____

Prefixes

A prefix is a special word part added to the beginning of a root word. Adding a prefix changes the meaning of the root word.

Example: *The prefix* **over** *means "more than" or "too much." Adding that prefix to the root word* eat *gives us the word* overeat, *which means "to eat too much."*

Directions: Use the prefixes and root words listed below to make new words. Check your word in the dictionary, then write the definition of the word on a separate piece of paper.

Prefix	Prefix Meaning	Root Words
re	again	do
dis	do the opposite of	view
un	not	happy
pre	before	fair
		test
		obey

_____ _____ _____

_____ _____ _____

_____ _____ _____

Challenge: Can you think of root words on your own? Come up with one new root word to add to each prefix above to create four new words.

Name _____

Prefixes

A prefix is a special word part added to the beginning of a root word. Adding a prefix changes the meaning of the root word.
Example: *The prefix* **mis** *means "wrong." By adding it to the root word* spell, *we get the word* misspell, *which means to spell wrong.*

Directions: Circle the word in each of the sentences below that begins with a prefix. Then write the prefix and the root word.

Prefixes: mis over im

---

1 I misspelled two words on the test today.

_____ + _____
     prefix   root word

2 Matt thought that riding his bike up the hill was impossible.

_____ + _____
     prefix   root word

3 My mom thinks she overpaid the cashier.

_____ + _____
     prefix   root word

18

Name _____

Suffixes

Suffixes are special word parts added to the ends of root words. Suffixes change the meaning of the root words.

Example: *The suffix **y** means "having." Adding **y** to the root word* cloud *gives us the word* cloudy. Cloudy *means "having clouds."*

Directions: The suffix *ful* is given in the center of the flower below. On each line in the petals, write a word with the suffix *ful* in it.

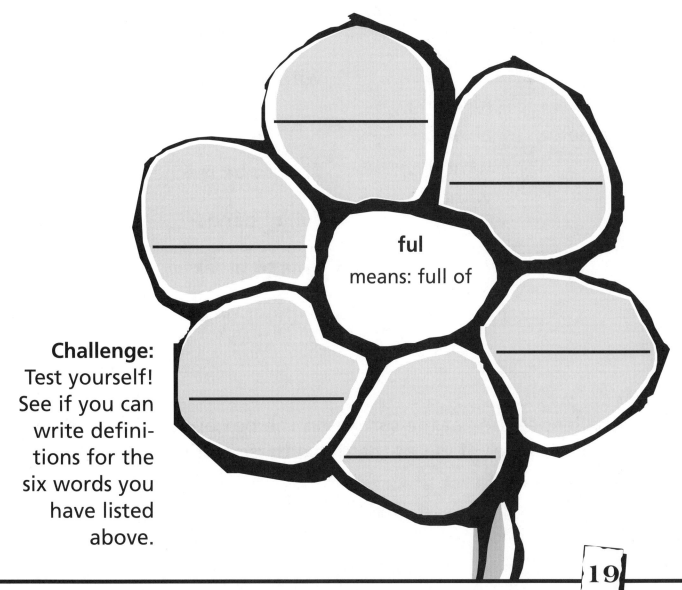

ful
means: full of

Challenge: Test yourself! See if you can write definitions for the six words you have listed above.

Name _____

Suffixes

Suffixes are special word parts added to the ends of root words.
Suffixes change the meaning of the root words.
Example*: The suffix* ful *means "full of." By adding* ful *to the root word* meaning, *we get the word* meaningful. Meaningful *means "full of meaning."*

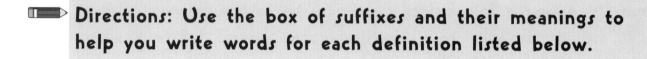

Directions: Use the box of suffixes and their meanings to help you write words for each definition listed below.

Suffix	Meaning
able	able to
y	having
less	without
ous	full of

1 without help _____

2 having rain _____

3 able to be reached _____

4 full of danger _____

5 able to break _____

6 without power _____

Challenge: Look at the suffixes in the box above. Think of your own examples of words that have these suffixes.

Name _____

Skill Check—Decoding Words

Prefixes

> **Directions:** Pair the prefixes *un* and *re* with the following root words to make new words. Write the meaning of each word. Use a separate piece of paper.

Prefix	Meaning	Root Words
un	not	wind
re	again	fold
		tie
		seal

Suffixes

> **Directions:** The suffix *er* means "more." Write the word with *er* for each of the definitions below.

1 More sweet _____

2 More great _____

3 More smart _____

Background

• Homophones, homographs, and contractions often present spelling challenges to learners. Once conquered, however, these spelling challenges become reading and writing tools that allow learners to readily absorb as well as clearly present written information. Working through the curriculum-based spelling activities in this section, learners will be able to hone spelling skills.

Homework Helper

• Working together with learners, choose a topic such as favorite animal, favorite sport, or favorite movie. Have the learner write six sentences about the topic, using at least two contractions in each sentence.

Research-based Activity

• Encyclopedias are great resources of information about our world. Have the learners find out more about arctic wolves (p. 23)—what they eat, how they are able to survive in the Arctic's harsh weather conditions, where in the Arctic do they live, etc.—by using an encyclopedia.

Test Prep

• The vocabulary skills in this section meet state standards for developing written and visual language.

Different Audiences

• The following words are homographs: content, finish, lead, lower, perfect, and tear. Ask the learners to write out the different meanings of each word with the help of a dictionary. Since some homographs are pronounced differently for each meaning, have the learners practice saying the words out loud.

22

Name _____

Homophones

Homophones are words that sound the same but are spelled differently and have different meanings.

Example: *The words* eight *and* ate *are homophones. While they sound the same,* eight *is a number and* ate *is the past tense of the verb "to eat."*

Directions: Read the sentences below about arctic wolves. Then choose the correct word to complete the sentences.

1 Arctic wolves have changed to fit _____ *(there, their)* surroundings.

2 The Arctic wolf can _____ *(see, sea)* very well.

3 The Arctic is not an easy place to live _____ *(four, for)* most animals.

4 Many animals have _____ *(to, too)* leave the Arctic during the winter.

5 Arctic wolves can stay _____ *(there, their)* even though the weather is very cold.

Challenge: Use the Internet to do some research about the Arctic on your own. What other animals live there? How have they adapted to their environment?

23

Name _____

Homographs

Homographs are words that are spelled the same, but have different meanings. Sometimes the words are pronounced the same and sometimes they are not.
Example: *The word* **fine** *can either mean an amount of money a person must pay after doing something wrong, or it can describe feeling very well.*

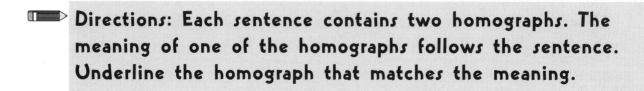

Directions: Each sentence contains two homographs. The meaning of one of the homographs follows the sentence. Underline the homograph that matches the meaning.

1 The puppy was happy when the **ground** meat fell on the **ground**.   *(floor)*

2 Mom asked me to **close** the door because I was **close** to it. *(near)*

3 The doctor **wound** a bandage around my **wound**. *(past tense of wind)*

4 The vegetable farmer hopes to **produce** a lot of **produce** this year.   *(make)*

5 As the dancer took her **bow** after the show, her **bow** came untied.   *(bend at the waist)*

6 "Be **patient**," the doctor said to her **patient**. *(person being treated by a doctor)*

Name _____

Contractions

A contraction is a short way to write two words together. Some letters are left out, with an apostrophe in their place.
Example: **I have** *can be shortened into the contraction* **I've.**

Directions: Write the correct contraction for the underlined word on the line at the end of each sentence below.

didn't	they'll	I'm	you've
wouldn't	We've	you'll	

1 My brother said he was sorry, so <u>I am</u> not upset with him anymore. _____

2 <u>We have</u> been waiting here for 30 minutes. _____

3 Jared told me that <u>you have</u> been his best friend for a long time. _____

4 Ryan <u>did not</u> eat the last cookie. _____

5 Susan knew she <u>would not</u> be ready to leave on time. _____

6 I hope <u>you will</u> be at the party. _____

7 <u>They will</u> play at the playground all afternoon. _____

Challenge: Listen to your family talk during breakfast tomorrow morning. Can you count how many contractions are used in their conversation?

Name _____

Contractions

A contraction is a short way to write two words together. Some letters are left out, with an apostrophe in their place.
Example: *The words* **do not** *can be shortened into the contraction* **don't**.

Directions: Circle the contraction in each sentence that is spelled incorrectly. Then write the contraction correctly.

1 Were going to the zoo to see the lions. _____

2 Th'ats my favorite book! _____

3 The girls arn't playing soccer today. _____

4 Shell have to write a report about Mars. _____

5 When Mom beeps the horn, we'ill know she is ready. _____

6 You'r very kind to help me with my homework. _____

Challenge:
Use the encyclopedia to find out information about lions. Share your information with your parents!

Name _____

Skill Check—Spelling

Homophones

Directions: Choose the correct word to finish each sentence.

1 My mother's sister is my _____. *(ant, aunt)*

2 We _____ baked tofu for dinner. *(eight, ate)*

3 The gum cost ten _____. *(scents, cents)*

Contractions

Directions: Replace the underlined words with contractions.

1 The boy <u>did not</u> know where the library was located in the

new town. _____

2 If Diana had known about the game, she <u>would have</u> come.

_____

3 The kids <u>have not</u> seen the new park yet. _____

4 <u>They are</u> planning to go to the market this weekend. _____

5 <u>I have</u> enough chocolate chips for the cookies. _____

6 That <u>is not</u> a cardinal; it's a blue jay. _____

Teaching Tips...

Background

• Editorial skills are important to vocabulary development. In order to develop strong sentences, learners must be able to apply editorial skills such as punctuation, spelling, and capitalization effectively. Practicing these editing conventions is necessary for learners to grow as writers and to communicate ideas to an audience.

Homework Helper

• Choose a local newspaper and have learners pick a story with which to work. Have the learners go through the first paragraph of the story and highlight instances where capitalization, question marks, periods, and commas are used.

Research-based Activity

• Using a variety of sources for finding information is important to build research skills. Have the learners locate a picture of the brain on the Internet and print out a copy of the image. Next have the learners label the cerebellum, which is described on page 30.

Test Prep

• The skills that are presented in this section are part of curriculum and state standards. The activities are geared toward preparing learners for testing these skills.

Different Audiences

• When working with ESL learners, have them write a passage describing a food from their country in their native language. Then have the learners translate the passage into English, applying the grammar and punctuation rules of English language arts.

TEACHING TIPS

Name _____

Capitalization

Capital letters are used to start the first word of sentences. Capital letters are also used for names of people and places.
Example: *simon lives in new jersey. To correct this sentence, we capitalize as follows: **S**imon lives in **N**ew **J**ersey.*

Directions: Use the rules of capitalization to rewrite the sentences below. If you need more space, use a separate piece of paper.

1 henry hudson discovered a river in north america.

_____

2 dutch settlers came to the area hudson discovered.

_____

3 families set up a colony on the island of manhattan.

_____

4 the colony was called new amsterdam.

_____

5 the leader of the colony was peter stuyvesant.

_____

6 new amsterdam later became new york city.

_____

Name _____

Punctuation: Question Marks and Periods

We use punctuation to make our writing clearer. We use a period to mark the end of a sentence and a question mark to mark the end of a question.

Example: *What kind of fruit do you like?*
I like apples.

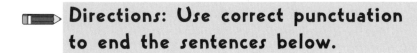 **Directions: Use correct punctuation to end the sentences below.**

1A How do your brain and body work together _____

B The cerebellum is the part of the brain that controls balance and movement in your body _____

2A What is your body's combination of balance and movement called _____

B It is called coordination_____

3A Your brain sends signals to your body parts _____

B The signals tell those parts to move _____

4A Where is the cerebellum located _____

B It is located toward the back of your head _____

Challenge: When you ask someone a series of questions about the same subject, it is called an interview. Interview one of your parents about their favorite sport. Write down the questions and answers. Make sure to use the correct punctuation.

Name _____

Spelling

*A word that names one thing is singular. A word that names more than one thing is plural. To make a singular word plural, we usually just add **s** to the end of that word.*
Example: Book *names one book.*

        Books *names more than one book.*

*For words that end in **s, ss, x, sh**, and **ch**, we add **es** to make them plural.*
Example: Beach *names one beach.*

        Beaches *names more than one beach.*

> **Directions: Write the plural form of the words that are underlined.**

1 The Statue of Liberty is in the form of a woman

   holding a <u>torch</u>. _____

2 A male <u>hippopotamus</u> weighs about five tons. _____

3 Short bushes and trees make up the <u>brush</u>. _____

4 The red <u>fox</u> lives in forest areas. _____

5 There is a <u>patch</u> of black on the dog's white fur._____

6 A <u>compass</u> is an instrument that can help you find the

   right direction. _____

Challenge: Using an encyclopedia, find out the history of the Statue of Liberty. Share your information with your parents.

Name _____

Commas

We use commas to separate words in a list. There is always a comma after the last word before **and***.*
Example: *It rained on Monday, Tuesday, and Wednesday.*

 Directions: Read the sentences below. Add commas where they are needed.

1 Some of the apple pie ingredients are sugar apples and cinnamon.

2 There is usually snow in December January and February.

3 Dogs cats fish and birds are popular pets.

4 I have a ruler a pencil a notebook and my lunch in my backpack.

5 Toronto Montreal and Ottawa are cities in Canada.

6 We will learn about science math and art this afternoon.

7 Red orange yellow and green are some of the colors in a rainbow.

Challenge: Name three more colors of a rainbow.

32

Name _____

Skill Check—Editing

Capitalization

✏➤ **Directions: Rewrite the following sentences. Use capital letters where they are needed.**

1 we are going to the movie theater in the town of montvale.

_____

2 carly, sydney, and I are planning a trip to florida.

_____

3 houston is a city in texas.

_____

Punctuation: Questions and Statements

✏➤ **Directions: Each line has two sentences. Rewrite them with the correct punctuation. Don't forget to use capital letters when necessary.**

1 What day is it _____

  Today is sunday _____

2 Carin is hungry _____

  what will she eat for lunch _____

3 Susan is planning a party _____

  Whom will she invite _____

Background

• To write creatively and effectively, learners must know how and when to apply writing strategies to their work. Using grammar rules to develop sentences is an integral part of curricula. These activities teach learners about building sentences as well as writing a variety of sentences.

Homework Helper

• To help learners grasp the differences between different types of sentences, create sentences that are statements, questions, and exclamations. Omit the ending punctuation and ask the learners to insert the right punctuation. Use the activities on pages 37 and 38 as guides for your sentences.

Research-based Activity

• Ask learners to use the library to find out the name of the planet closest to the Sun. Have them compare and contrast this planet to Pluto, which is featured in the activity on page 35.

Test Prep

• The following activities are based on state standards and prepare learners for test formats as well as test content.

Different Audiences

• For accelerated learners, have them create a story about a specific event that happened to them. Ask the learners to incorporate the skills—conjunctions, statements, questions, and exclamations—that are presented in this section.

Name _____

Incomplete Sentences

A **complete sentence** contains a complete idea. It has a subject and a verb.

Example: *The boy won the race.*
*In this sentence **boy** is the subject and **won** is the verb.*

An **incomplete sentence** is missing information.

Example: *Eggs for breakfast.*
*Correct sentence: **She** (subject) **likes** (verb) eggs for breakfast.*

> **Directions: Put a C in front of the complete sentences below and an I in front of the incomplete sentences.**

1 _____ Nine planets in our solar system.

2 _____ Planets are bodies that travel around the Sun.

3 _____ Pluto is the planet farthest from the Sun.

4 _____ Pluto also the smallest planet.

5 _____ A very cold planet.

6 _____ Scientists have a difficult time studying Pluto.

7 _____ Because it is too far away.

8 _____ Scientists believe Pluto is made up of rock and ice.

Name _____

Conjunctions

The word **and** is a conjunction. Conjunctions are words used to join parts of sentences.

Example: *I finished my homework. I watched television.*
*I finished my homework **and** watched television.*
Always check your verbs once you have changed the sentences.
If you have two subjects, then the verb will change.
Example: *Mike is going to the movies. James is going to the movies.*
*Mike and James **are** going to the movies.*

Directions: Join the sentences below using the word and. If you need more space, use a separate sheet of paper.

1 Plants need light to grow. Plants need water to grow.

_____

2 Oahu is an island in the state of Hawaii. Maui is an island in Hawaii.

_____

3 Benjamin Franklin was a scientist. He was a politician.

_____

4 The United States is in North America. Mexico is in North America.

_____